Longman Practice Exam Papers

GCSE Science

Emily Sadler and John Sadler

Series editors:

Geoff Black and Stuart Wall

Titles available for GCSE

Biology

Chemistry

Mathematics (Intermediate)

Mathematics (Higher)

Physics

Science

Addison Wesley Longman Ltd,
Edinburgh Gate, Harlow,
CM20 2JE, England
and Associated Companies throughout the World

First published 1998

ISBN 0 852 35649 0

British Library Cataloguing-in-Publication Data
A catalogue record for this book is available from the British Library.

Set in Times 11/13pt

Printed by Henry Ling Ltd at The Dorset Press, Dorchester, Dorset

Contents

Editors' preface   iv

Acknowledgements   iv

How to use this book   1

Foundation paper 1   3

Foundation paper 2   9

Foundation paper 3   14

Higher paper 1   21

Higher paper 2   29

Higher paper 3   36

Solutions to practice exam papers   44

How well did you do?   59

Periodic Table   60

Editors' preface

Longman Practice Exam Papers are written by experienced GCSE examiners and teachers. They will provide you with an ideal opportunity to practise under exam-type conditions before your actual school or college mocks or before the GCSE examination itself. As well as becoming familiar with the vital skill of pacing yourself through a whole exam paper, you can check your answers against examiner solutions and mark-schemes to assess the level you have reached.

Longman Practice Exam Papers can be used alongside the *Longman GCSE Study Guides* and *Longman Exam Practice Kits* to provide a comprehensive range of home study support as you prepare to take your GCSE in each subject covered.

Acknowledgements

We are very grateful for the help of the staff at Addison Wesley Longman, in particular Bridget Allen and Linda Marsh who have worked wonders in getting this book together under a most taxing timetable.

Finally, we thank our families for their patience and for their encouragement during the preparation of this book.

EMILY SADLER AND JOHN SADLER

How to use this book

- This book is designed to help you to prepare for your GCSE examination. The questions are set at the same standard as the GCSE examination. The aim is to ensure that you attain the highest level that you can get. By using this book carefully and sensibly you will be able to use the information supplied by the authors to improve your grades and ensure success.

- Try to take the tests under GCSE conditions. A quiet room, plus all the necessary equipment and a clock is ideal. Use the marking scheme to check on your performance.

- Remember that the paper will include a copy of the Periodic Table, so you do not have to learn every element and its symbol.

- The Foundation Tier papers are aimed at students who are expected to get grades C to G; the Higher Tier papers are for students expected to get grades A* to D. Do not despair if you cannot do the Higher papers – the examination is trying to find out what you know, understand and can do. This should be your attitude too; that you will show the examiner what you can do. Remember this – examiners are trying to find out what you know, hence only questions that are on your syllabus are set.

- Read the questions at least twice and underline key words. You will score no marks unless you answer the questions asked.

- You may find some questions more difficult to answer than others, do not be put off by this. Try your best to answer the question – you may find that you score some marks.

- Always make sure that your answers are concise and relevant.

- Make sure you keep an eye on the clock and check your progress every 15 minutes. Do not spend all your time trying to answer one question – you must try to attempt them all. If you get stuck on a question, leave it and come back to it later.

- If you manage to finish early, go back and check your work. Do NOT make any changes unless you are certain that you have made a mistake. Your first instinct is usually the right one.

- The number of lines under each sub-question indicates how much detail is required, as does the mark for each section. If there are three marks available for a question then you must make sure that you have at least three separate points in your answer.

- If the question involves you solving a problem make sure that you show all your working. There are marks for the method you adopt as well as for the correct answer with the correct units.

- Make sure that you have all the necessary equipment – calculator (preferably with new batteries), pencils, pens, rubber, ruler.

- Make sure any diagrams are neatly drawn and clearly labelled.

- Most important, be positive – it is never too early to start revision. If you feel you have under-performed in any of these test papers, spend time revising that particular topic and try the test again.

- There are answers and tips for each of the question papers. If you are not sure that your answer is correct, ask your teacher or another responsible person – do not be too over-generous with yourself – it might give you undue expectations.

- Make sure that you have answered ALL the questions – even if you think you do not know the answer, guess. You cannot lose marks!

Using these practice exam papers

In this book there are three Foundation papers and three Higher papers, made up as follows:

Paper	Time (mins)	Marks
Foundation 1	60	60
Foundation 2	60	60
Foundation 3	60	60
Higher 1	60	60
Higher 2	60	60
Higher 3	60	60

The answers and mark-schemes to these papers are given at the end of the papers. Use these to check your answers **after** you have attempted to answer the questions to the best of your ability. Try to answer all the questions – do not give up too easily.

Attempt the Foundation Tier papers first – if you score more than 125 marks altogether you should attempt the Higher Tier papers – if less than 125 marks you will need to do more revision.

Longman Examination Board

General Certificate of Secondary Education

Science (Double award)

Foundation Paper 1

Time: 60 minutes

Instructions

■ Answer **all** the questions.

■ Write your answers in the spaces provided.

■ Use a blue or black ink or ball-point pen.

■ Show all stages in any calculations and state the units.

Information for candidates

■ The number of marks is given in brackets at the end of each question or part-question. The total mark for the question is given at the end of the question.

■ Marks will **not** be deducted for wrong answers.

■ This paper has 6 questions.

■ The maximum mark for this paper is 60.

Number	Mark
1.	
2.	
3.	
4.	
5.	
6.	

---

1. The diagram below shows the digestive tract of a pig.

Leave margin blank

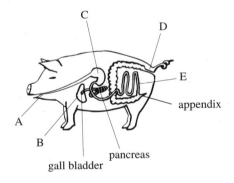

Name the parts A to E and give **one** function for each part.

Part	Name	Function
A	Mouth	To consume food
B	Liver	remove poison or store Glucose
C	Stomach	to digests food
D	Rectum	Stores waste temporely
E	Small intestines	absorbs soluble food

(10 Marks)

Total: 10 marks

Turn over

2. Look at the food web in the diagram below, then answer the questions that follow.

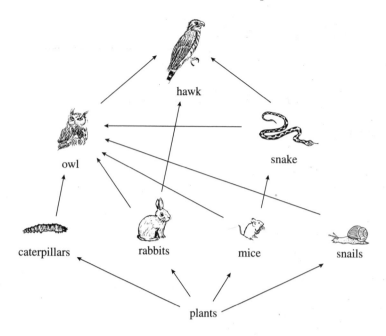

(a) Why must food webs always start with plants, e.g. grass and trees?

Every Mammal eats plants; only plants can convert energy from the sun into food .

(1 mark)

(b) What do the arrows represent in the food web?

....

(1 mark)

(c) Which of the items are:

(i) herbivores Mammals which only eat Plants ....

(ii) secondary consumers ....

(2 marks)

(d) Complete this sentence:

The number of consumers depends on the number of ....

(1 mark)

(e) For the food web shown above, draw a pyramid of

(i) numbers

(2 marks)

(ii) biomass

(2 marks)

(f) What information is obtained from a pyramid of biomass that is not obtained from a pyramid of numbers?

....

(1 mark)

Total: 10 marks

3. Fill in the gaps to complete the sentences below by choosing words from the following list. Each word may be used once, more than once or not at all.

carbon dioxide   nucleus

cells   oxygen

chlorophyll   photosynthesis

chloroplasts   roots

genes   soil

leaves   Sun

Inside many of the cells of green plants are small structures called ......*cells*............... They are very small, less than 0.0004 mm across. They contain ..*chlorophyll*..... This is where ..*photosynthesis*.. takes place.

water + ..*carbon dioxide*.. + energy → carbohydrates + ..*carbon dioxide*.. oxygen

The energy is obtained from the ..*sun leaves*... Sun

The atmosphere contains only 0.03% of ..*carbon dioxide*.. , but this is enough for the photosynthesis of all the world's green plants. Water is obtained from the ..*roots soil*.....

The ..*roots*................ of the green plants absorb the water. This is then carried through the stem to the ..*leaves*............ .

(10 marks)

Total: 10 marks

4. The diagram below shows part of the human breathing system.

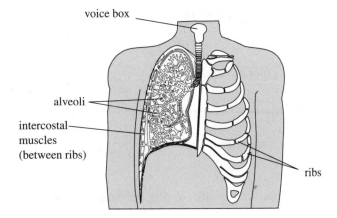

(a) Fill in the gaps in the table on page 6 which describes the part of the breathing system and its function. (The first one has been done for you.)

Turn over

Part of the breathing system	What it does
alveoli	sites of gaseous exchange
	a muscle sheet
intercostal muscles	
	organs of respiration
ribs	
	connects lungs to mouth and nose

(5 marks)

(b) What is the difference between breathing and respiration?

..... breathing is inhaling and exhaling of yg ....

....

(2 marks)

(c) What is the advantage of alveoli being thin and covered with capillaries?

....

(1 mark)

(d) The table below compares the composition of air breathed in and air breathed out.

	Air breathed in	Air breathed out
nitrogen	79 %	79 %
oxygen	21 %	17 %
carbon dioxide	0.03 %	4 %

Explain why

(i) the percentage of nitrogen remains constant

....

(1 mark)

(ii) the volume of oxygen decreases and the volume of carbon dioxide increases

....

....

(2 marks)

(iii) exhaled air can still be used in the 'kiss of life' to help revive ill people.

....

(1 mark)

(e) Why does smoking by pregnant women often result in them producing babies with a lower birth weight than normal?

....

(1 mark)

Total: 13 marks

5. When you touch something very hot with your hand, your hand immediately jumps away from the hot surface.

(a) What name is given to this type of action?

....

(1 mark)

(b) Name two main parts that make up the central nervous system.

.... and ....

(2 marks)

(c) Name the sense organ (receptor) that responds to the following stimuli. (The first one has been done for you.)

   (i) hearing   ear

   (ii) taste   ....

   (iii) touch   ....

   (iv) temperature   ....

(3 marks)

(d) What is the function of each of the following parts of the eye?

   (i) cornea ....

   (ii) retina ....

   (iii) optic nerve ....

(3 marks)

Total: 9 marks

6. The following results were obtained when taking measurements in a class of pupils.

Colour of eyes	brown	blue	green	grey
	11	6	3	5
Type of hair	very curly	curly	wavy	straight
	3	6	7	9
Colour of hair	brown	black	ginger	blonde
	9	5	3	8

Turn over

(a) How many pupils were there in the class?

....

(1 mark)

(b) What percentage of the pupils have blonde hair?

....

(1 mark)

The differences between individuals of a species are called variations.

(c) Suggest two other variations that could have been measured by the pupils.

....

....

(2 marks)

(d) Give an example of a

(i) continuous variation ....

(1 mark)

(ii) discontinuous variation ....

(1 mark)

(e) Give two factors that might affect variation of individuals in a species.

....

....

(2 marks)

Total: 8 marks

Longman Examination Board

General Certificate of Secondary Education

Science (Double award)

Foundation Paper 2

Time: 60 minutes

Instructions

- Answer **all** the questions.

- Write your answers in the spaces provided.

- Use a blue or black ink or ball-point pen.

- Show all stages in any calculations and state the units.

Information for candidates

- The number of marks is given in brackets at the end of each question or part-question. The total mark for the question is given at the end of the question.

- Marks will **not** be deducted for wrong answers.

- This paper has 6 questions.

- The maximum mark for this paper is 60.

Number	Mark
1.	
2.	
3.	
4.	
5.	
6.	

---

1. By referring ONLY to the first 18 elements in the Periodic Table, name:

    (a) (i) an element in the same period as silicon ....

    (ii) a liquid element that is in the same group as chlorine ....

    (iii) the element that has the highest relative atomic mass ....

    (iv) an element that is monatomic ....

    (v) a yellow solid that reacts with oxygen to give a colourless gas ....

    (vi) the commonest metal ....

    (vii) the three commonest elements present in pure air, in order of abundance. Commonest element first.

    1 .... 2 .... 3 ....

    (8 marks)

Leave margin blank

Turn over

(b) Why is the relative atomic mass of chlorine not a whole number?

....

....

(2 marks)

Total: 10 marks

2. The first box shows the arrangement of particles in a liquid.

(a) Draw, in the boxes below, the arrangement of particles in a solid and a gas.

solid   gas

(3 marks)

(b) Spray-on furniture polish is a mixture of wax and a solvent such as ethanol. The ethanol evaporates and leaves a layer of wax. Describe what happens to the ethanol particles during the process of evaporation.

....

....

(2 marks)

(c) The change from liquid to gas is called evaporation. What is the name for each of the following changes?

(i) liquid to solid ....

(ii) solid to gas ....

(2 marks)

Total: 7 marks

3. The statements below refer to different types of changes. Draw a line to link each type of change and an example of that type of change. The first one has been done for you.

Type of change	Example
endothermic reaction	hydrochloric acid plus sodium hydroxide
neutralisation	adding potassium nitrate to water
displacement	propane to propene plus hydrogen
exothermic reaction	heating ammonium chloride to give ammonia and hydrogen chloride which recombine on cooling
hydration	glucose in the presence of enzymes giving ethanol and carbon dioxide
fermentation	anhydrous copper(II) sulphate reacting with water
reduction	hydrogen burning in chlorine to give hydrogen chloride
reversible reaction	sodium sulphate reacting with barium chloride to give insoluble barium sulphate and sodium chloride
precipitation	iron reacting with copper(II) sulphate
cracking	magnesium burning in oxygen

Total: 9 marks

4. Aluminium can be made from aluminium oxide by heating powdered magnesium with aluminium oxide in an atmosphere of argon.

(a) Write the word equation for the preparation of aluminium from aluminium oxide and magnesium.

....

(2 marks)

(b) Name another metal that could be used instead of magnesium. Give a reason for your choice.

....

....

(2 marks)

(c) Magnesium is in Group 2 and period 3 of the Periodic Table. In the same way describe the position of aluminium.

Group .... Period ....

(2 marks)

(d) Suggest why

(i) the reaction is carried out in an atmosphere of argon

....

(ii) magnesium powder is used and not magnesium ribbon

....

(2 marks)

Turn over

(e) Use the Periodic Table to write down the number of protons, the number of neutrons and the number of electrons in the aluminium ion Al^{3+}.

protons .... neutrons .... electrons ....

(3 marks)

(f) By what process is aluminium extracted industrially?

....

(1 mark)

Total: 12 marks

5. The diagram below represents part of the natural process that occurs during the rock cycle.

(a) Under what types of conditions are the following types of rocks formed?

(i) sedimentary rocks

....

....

(ii) igneous rocks

....

....

(iii) metamorphic rocks

....

....

(6 marks)

(b) Give an example of each type of rock

sedimentary ....

igneous ....

metamorphic ....

(3 marks)

(c) (i) What type of rocks often contain fossils? ....:

(i) How can fossils be used to determine the age of rock?

....

....

(3 marks)

(d) Explain why the crystals formed at X are smaller than those formed at Y.

....

(1 mark)

(e) Explain how weathering is caused by:

(i) the freezing of water

....

(ii) acid rain

....

(2 marks)

Total: 15 marks

6. Methane and ethene are both hydrocarbons. Both occur naturally. Ethene is given off by fruits (particularly bananas) as they ripen.

(a) Where does methane occur?

....

(1 mark)

(b) Suggest, with a reason, a precaution that must be taken when transporting large amounts of bananas.

....

....

(2 marks)

(c) When methane and ethene burn in a limited supply of air, the gases burn incompletely. Other than water and carbon dioxide, name two substances that might be formed.

.... and ....

(2 marks)

(d) Fill in the missing word in the following sentence.

When hydrocarbon fuels burn, large quantities of carbon dioxide are put into the atmosphere; this makes a big contribution to the .... effect.

(1 mark)

(e) Give the formula of the substance formed when the elements of water (H_2O) are removed from ethanol (C_2H_5OH).

....

(1 mark)

Total: 7 marks

Turn over

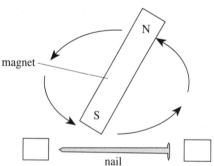

Longman Examination Board

General Certificate of Secondary Education

Science (Double award)

Foundation Paper 3

Time: 60 minutes

Instructions

■ Answer **all** the questions.

■ Write your answers in the spaces provided.

■ Use a blue or black ink or ball-point pen.

■ Show all stages in any calculations and state the units.

Information for candidates

■ The number of marks is given in brackets at the end of each question or part-question. The total mark for the question is given at the end of the question.

■ Marks will **not** be deducted for wrong answers.

■ This paper has 6 questions.

■ The maximum mark for this paper is 60.

Number	Mark
1.	
2.	
3.	
4.	
5.	
6.	

---

1. An iron nail can be magnetised by stroking it with a magnet, as shown in the diagram below.

Leave margin blank

(a) (i) Show on the diagram the end that becomes the south pole and the end that becomes the north pole of the nail.

(1 mark)

(ii) Using the nail and a piece of string, how would you show that the nail had become magnetised?

....

....

(2 marks)

(b) The diagram below shows a magnet attracting some iron nails.

    magnet

    nails

(i) What is the upward force on the nails?

....

(1 mark)

(ii) What is the downward force on the nails?

....

(1 mark)

(iii) Explain why more than one nail is attracted.

....

....

(2 marks)

(iv) How could this experiment be adapted to compare the strengths of magnets?

....

....

(2 marks)

(c) The student tried to pick up a nail using the apparatus shown. The electromagnet was not strong enough. However, when he placed an iron rod in the coil, he succeeded in picking up the nail.

    nail

(i) Explain why putting an iron rod in the coil increased the strength of the electromagnet.

....

(ii) Give one other way that he could have made the electromagnet stronger.

....

(2 marks)

Turn over

One of the advantages of an electromagnet is it can be switched on and off.

(d) Give one use of an electromagnet that makes use of this property.

....

(1 mark)

Total: 12 marks

2. The diagram below shows Emma and Lucy having their hair cut, sitting in front of plane mirrors.

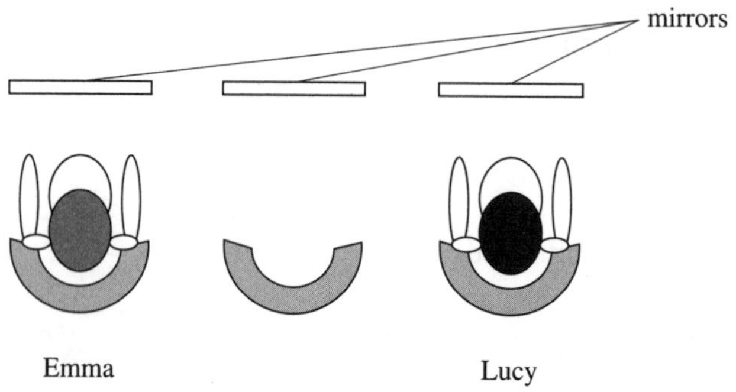

mirrors

Emma   Lucy

(a) Tick (✓) the statements that are true and put a cross (✗) against those statements that are NOT true

(i) Emma can see herself by reflection.

(ii) The image of Lucy is as far behind the mirror as she is in front of the mirror.

(iii) Lucy's image is larger than Lucy herself.

(iv) The image of Emma is laterally inverted.

(v) Less light is reflected than entered the mirror.

(5 marks)

(b) Emma can see Lucy's image in the middle mirror. Draw light rays on the diagram above to show how this is possible.

(3 marks)

(c) The diagram below shows a boy trying to catch a fish with a spear.

X

In order to hit the fish will he have to aim (A) at the fish (B) slightly higher than the fish (C) slightly lower than the fish. Explain your answer.

....

....

....

(3 marks)

(d) Explain why, if the fish was at position X the fish would not be able to see the boy.

....

(1 mark)

Total: 12 marks

3. When a noisy lorry or car passes your house it can make the window panes rattle.

(a) What does this tell you about sound?

....

(1 mark)

You are told that on the Sun there are continuous nuclear explosions.

(b) Explain why you cannot hear the noise of these explosions.

....

(1 mark)

Sound travels through water. Ultrasound is used by ships to measure the depth of water.

(c)　(i)　What is 'ultrasound'?

....

(1 mark)

(ii) Describe, briefly, how ultrasound can be used to measure the depth of water.

....

....

(2 marks)

(iii) Give one other use of ultrasound.

....

(1 mark)

Turn over

(d) Musical sounds have the following characteristics: loudness, pitch and quality.

Lance listens to his radio. He uses the volume and tone controls to alter the sound.

(i) Lance increases the volume. Using a cathode ray oscilloscope he was able to show the shape of the wave before he altered the volume. In the space, draw the shape of the wave after he increases the loudness.

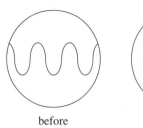

before   after

(2 marks)

(ii) Lance then increases the pitch (tone). In the space below, draw the shape obtained.

(2 marks)

Total: 10 marks

4. An electric heater has two heating elements. The elements are shown in the diagram below.

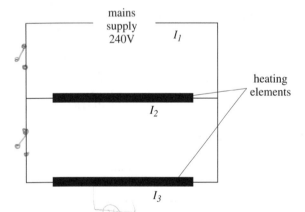

(a) Explain why the heating elements are placed in parallel instead of in series.

....

....

(2 marks)

(b) Jamie wants to measure the voltage across one of the heating elements. Draw a voltmeter on the diagram to show how he does this.

(1 mark)

(c) A new model of the heater is available. It has switches which allow none, one or both heating elements to be used. Draw to the right of the above diagram the circuit diagram for the new model.

(2 marks)

(d) The total resistance of both elements is 60 ohms. Circle the size of fuse that should be used. Give a reason for your answer

3 A   5 A   13 A   15A

....

(2 marks)

(e) The diagram below shows the plug used for the heater. Fill in the missing labels on the diagram.

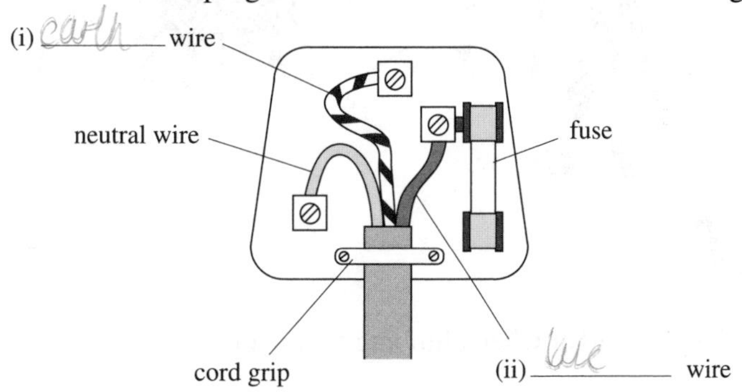

(i) *earth* wire

neutral wire

fuse

cord grip

(ii) *live* wire

(2 marks)

(f) Explain how the fuse in the plug works.

the filament if too much current passes through -heat melts filament circuit broken

(2 marks)

(g) The cost of electricity is 7.0p per unit (per kilowatt-hour). Calculate the cost of running the heater, with both elements on, for 10 hours.

P=IV P=960   9.6

....

(2 marks)

Total: 13 marks

5. Fill in the gaps to complete the following sentences.

(a) The solar system means a system attached to the (i) *Sun* The nine planets in the solar system are: Earth; Jupiter; (ii) *Mars*; Mercury; Neptune; Pluto; Saturn; Uranus and Venus.

Jupiter

(iii) *Saturn* is the largest planet and (iv) *pluto* is the smallest planet. All the planets move around the Sun in elliptical paths called (v) *orbits* The planet nearest the Sun is (vi) *mercury*

Most of the planets have (vii) *moons* revolving around them.

(7 marks)

(b) Give two differences between planets and stars.

Planets do not have light, reflect light from Sun. Planets orbit Stars

(2 marks)

Total: 9 marks

Turn over

6. A hang-glider carries his equipment to the top of a cliff. He then jumps off the cliff and later returns to ground level.

(a) What form of energy does the glider gain when climbing to the top of the cliff?

.... *gravitational   P E* ....

(1 mark)

(b) What form of energy does the glider gain when he jumps off the cliff?

.... *gravitational* ....

(1 mark)

(c) Explain why the glider stays in the air.

.... *the sail has a large mass so wind is trapped under keeps it in air* ....

(1 mark)

(d) Apart from temperature, suggest why gliders prefer to glide on warm days rather than cold days.

.... *wind, not as cold because cold high* ....

....

(1 mark)

Total: 4 marks

Longman Examination Board

General Certificate of Secondary Education

Science (Double award)

Higher Paper 1

Time: 60 minutes

Instructions

- Answer **all** the questions.

- Write your answers in the spaces provided.

- Use a blue or black ink or ball-point pen.

- Show all stages in any calculations and state the units.

Information for candidates

- The number of marks is given in brackets at the end of each question or part-question. The total mark for the question is given at the end of the question.

- Marks will **not** be deducted for wrong answers.

- This paper has 5 questions.

- The maximum mark for this paper is 60.

Number	Mark
1.	
2.	
3.	
4.	
5.	

---

1. The body has two main control systems (i) control of temperature and (ii) control of water.

   The graph below represents volumes of sweat and urine eliminated by a human being over a period of three days.

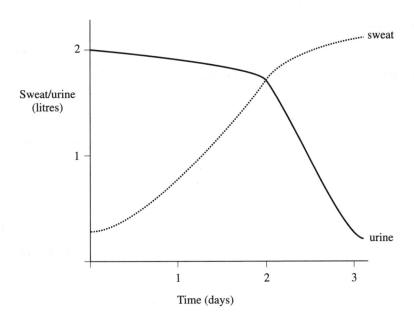

Leave margin blank

Turn over

(a) What is the biological name for keeping temperature and water content constant?

....

(1 mark)

(b) Deduce the probable weather conditions for:

(i) day 1 ....

(ii) day 2 ....

(iii) day 3 ....

(3 marks)

(c) (i) Give two ways in which the skin acts to keep the body cool in hot weather.

....

....

(ii) Give two other roles of the skin.

....

....

(4 marks)

(d) Suggest reasons for the following:

(i) When water is drunk in large amounts a large volume of urine is passed and the urine is pale in colour.

....

....

(ii) When a person has sweated a great deal, little urine is passed and the urine is much darker in colour.

....

....

(4 marks)

(e) Explain why the elimination of water by the kidneys can be considered as:

(i) excretion

....

(ii) osmo-regulation

....

(2 marks)

Total: 14 marks

2. The table below shows the percentage of water and the amount of energy (in kilojoules) in 1 kilogram (kg) of certain foods.

Food	% water	energy value kJ/kg
Beef steak	50	11.4
Boiled egg	70	7.0
Cheese	30	16.0
White fish	80	4.6
Lettuce	90	2.3

(a) Plot these figures on the graph below, plotting the percentage of water on the *x*-axis and energy value on the *y*-axis. Label each point on your graph with the name of the food.

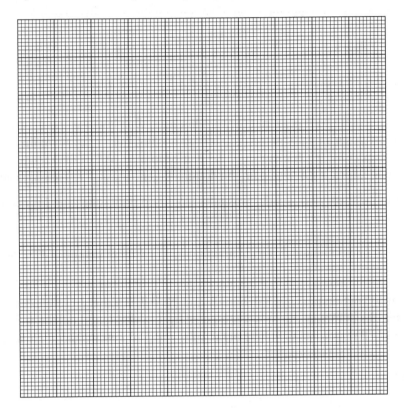

(4 marks)

(b) From the graph, deduce the relationship between energy value and water content.

....

(1 mark)

(c) A certain brand of butter contains 20% water. From the graph, deduce its energy content in kJ/kg.

....

(1 mark)

(d) What is the one source of energy for these foods?

....

(1 mark)

Turn over

Leave margin blank

(e) What is represented by the point on the graph of (100,0)?

....

(1 mark)

Total: 8 marks

3. (a) What are each of the following:

(i) alleles

....

(ii) genes

....

(iii) gametes

....

(3 marks)

In 1865 Mendel, after experimenting with peas, put forward his laws. One law was the Law of segregation – 'Genes normally occur in pairs in the ordinary body cells, but segregate in the formation of eggs or sperm (sex cells), each member of the pair becoming part of the separate sex cell. When egg and sperm unite, forming a gene pair, the dominant gene masks the recessive gene.'

(b) Mendel's contribution to the theory of genetics was not recognised until long after his death. Suggest a reason for this.

....

(1 mark)

(c) Mendel's work was carried out on peas, the tall variety and the dwarf variety. (Alleles are represented by a single letter; the dominant allele is represented by a capital letter and the recessive allele by a small letter.) If **P** represents the allele in tall peas and p represents the allele in dwarf peas; show how Mendel was able to produce:

(i) only tall peas

(ii) only dwarf peas

(iii) seeds that produced a three in four chance of producing tall peas

(4 marks)

(d) Draw a genetic diagram to show that there was an equal chance of you being a girl or a boy.

(2 marks)

(e) Explain the meanings of the following terms:

  (i) selective breeding ....

....

  (ii) cloning ....

....

(2 marks)

Total: 12 marks

4. Photosynthesis is the process that occurs in green plants whereby carbon dioxide and water combine to produce biomass and oxygen.

(a) What else is required for photosynthesis to take place?

....

....

(2 marks)

(b) Write the balanced chemical equation for photosynthesis.

....

(2 marks)

The diagram below shows the cross section of a leaf.

Turn over

(c) Suggest advantages for each of the following:

(i) the leaves are flat and thin

....

....

(ii) the leaves have a coating of a waxy, transparent cuticle

....

....

(iii) palisade cells being near the tops of the leaves and packed in 'columns'

....

....

(6 marks)

(d) Pond weed was placed in a test tube as shown in the diagram and the following experiments carried out.

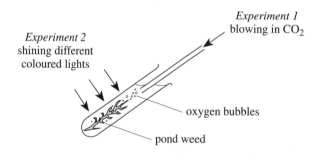

Experiment 2
shining different
coloured lights

Experiment 1
blowing in CO_2

oxygen bubbles

pond weed

Experiment 1

The number of bubbles of oxygen given off were counted before and after blowing in carbon dioxide. The results were:

	Number of bubbles of O_2 per minute
Before blowing in carbon dioxide	75
After blowing in carbon dioxide	160

Experiment 2

Various coloured lights were shone on the pond weed and the number of bubbles of oxygen given off were counted. The results were:

Colour of light	**Number of oxygen bubbles per minute**
blue	12
green	25
yellow	33
red	103

What can you deduce from these experiments?

(i) Experiment 1 ....

(1 mark)

(ii) Experiment 2 ....

....

(2 marks)

(e) Complete the following sentences.

Glucose is converted into:

(i) insoluble .... for storing in roots, stems and leaves

(ii) .... for storing in seeds

(iii) .... for making cell walls

(3 marks)

Total: 16 marks

5. The diagram below shows a cross section of a mammalian heart.

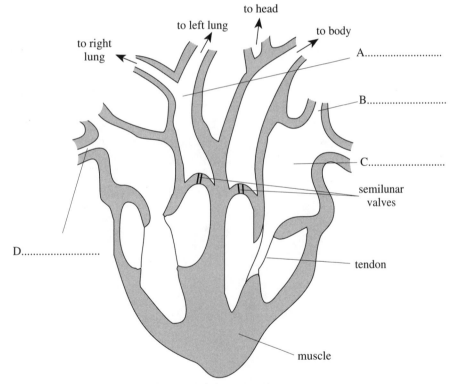

(a) On the diagram, complete the labels A, B, C and D.

(4 marks)

(b) The blood entering at B is oxygenated. Name the organ where blood becomes oxygenated.

....

(1 mark)

Turn over

(c) Complete the following table comparing arteries and veins.

	Arteries	Veins
blood direction	away from the heart	
pressure of blood		low
structure		thin, contains valves

(3 marks)

(d) A person is a heavy smoker. What effect would this have on:

(i) the arteries?

....

(ii) the person's general health?

....

(2 marks)

Total: 10 marks

Longman Examination Board

General Certificate of Secondary Education
Science (Double award)
Higher Paper 2

Time: 60 minutes

Instructions

- Answer **all** the questions.
- Write your answers in the spaces provided.
- Use a blue or black ink or ball-point pen.
- Show all stages in any calculations and state the units.

Information for candidates

- The number of marks is given in brackets at the end of each question or part-question. The total mark for the question is given at the end of the question.
- Marks will **not** be deducted for wrong answers.
- This paper has 5 questions.
- The maximum mark for this paper is 60.

Number	Mark
1.	
2.	
3.	
4.	
5.	

---

1. Name in each case:

   (a) an acid that does not contain oxygen ....

   (b) a metal that is manufactured by electrolysis ....

   (c) a sedimentary rock ....

   (d) a compound with ionic bonding ....

   (4 marks)

   Total: 4 marks

Leave margin blank

Turn over

2. The table below shows the formula and boiling point of a number of alkanes.

Alkane	Formula	Boiling point °C
hexane	C_6H_{14}	69
heptane	C_7H_{16}	99
octane	C_8H_{18}	126
nonane		151
decane	$C_{10}H_{22}$	174
undecane	$C_{11}H_{24}$	
dodecane	$C_{12}H_{26}$	216

(a) (i) What is the formula of nonane? ....

(ii) Suggest the boiling point of undecane. ....

(2 marks)

(b) Which alkane in the above table will have the lowest melting point?

....

(1 mark)

(c) Paraffin is obtained by the fractional distillation of crude oil. Paraffin contains a mixture of alkanes with a boiling range of 170 °C to 250 °C.

Which alkanes in the above table are present in paraffin?

....

....

(2 marks)

(d) The next member of the series is tridecane ($C_{13}H_{28}$). Tridecane can be cracked using the apparatus shown below.

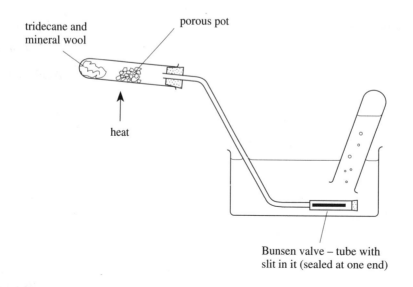

tridecane and mineral wool

porous pot

heat

Bunsen valve – tube with slit in it (sealed at one end)

(i) Suggest why the tube containing tridecane slopes downwards.

....

(ii) What is the purpose of the Bunsen valve?

....

(iii) Tridecane cracks into two products; one of the products is nonene (C_9H_{18}), name the other product.

....

(3 marks)

(e) Propene is a monomer that is used to make the polymer polypropene.

(i) What is a monomer?

....

(1 mark)

(ii) Draw the monomer propene.

(2 marks)

(iii) Draw a diagram of 3 propene molecules joined together to show the structure of polypropene.

(3 marks)

(iv) Suggest why when propene burns in a plentiful supply of air it produces carbon dioxide and water, whereas polypropene burns to give a mixture of carbon, carbon monoxide, carbon dioxide and water.

....

(1 mark)

Total: 15 marks

Turn over

3. The apparatus shown below was used to demonstrate the electrolysis of lime-water (calcium hydroxide (Ca(OH)$_2$)) dissolved in water.

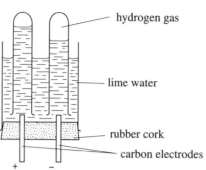

(a) Hydrogen gas is formed at the anode. Write a balanced ionic equation, including state symbols, for the discharge of hydrogen ions.

....

(2 marks)

(b) After a period of time, a white precipitate of calcium carbonate was formed. Give reasons for the formation of this compound.

....

....

....

(3 marks)

(c) The current was passed for several hours and eventually the white precipitate completely disappeared, leaving a colourless solution. Explain this observation.

....

....

(2 marks)

(d) When the colourless solution from (c) was heated, a white precipitate was formed. What is this white precipitate?

....

(1 mark)

(e) When a solution of lime-water is boiled in a test tube, a white precipitate of calcium hydroxide settles on the bottom of the test tube. What does this experiment tell you?

....

(1 mark)

(f) Calcium hydroxide has many industrial uses. Suggest why calcium hydroxide is:

(i) added by farmers to their land

....

(ii) preferred to sodium hydroxide for neutralising acid waste materials

....

(2 marks)

Total: 11 marks

4. Seven sets of students were asked to find the formula of an oxide of copper using the apparatus shown in the diagram.

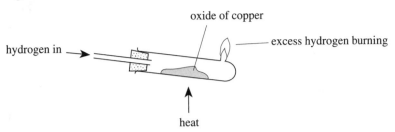

(a) (i) What other product will be formed apart from copper?

....

(ii) Why is it important to make sure that all the air is removed from the apparatus before heating the oxide of copper?

....

....

(2 marks)

(b) The results obtained were:

Set of students	A	B	C	D	E	F	G
Mass of copper	24.0	4.0	8.0	12.0	10.0	16.0	20.0
Mass of oxygen	6.0	1.0	2.0	3.0	2.5	3.5	5.0

(i) Suggest the three weighings the students might have made.

....

....

(3 marks)

(ii) Draw a graph of mass of copper (*y*-axis) against mass of oxygen (*x*-axis).

(4 marks)

Turn over

(iii) Which student's set of results should be ignored?

....

(1 mark)

(c) From the graph, what mass of copper reacts with 1.6 grams of oxygen?

....

(1 mark)

(d) From your answer to (c), work out the formula of this oxide of copper.

....

....

....

(3 marks)

(e) Name another metal oxide whose formula could be found by this method.

....

(1 mark)

Total: 15 marks

5. Carbon disulphide (CS_2) is a colourless liquid with a boiling point of 46 °C.

Carbon disulphide is an excellent solvent for sulphur.

Carbon disulphide is very inflammable and burns to give a mixture of sulphur dioxide and carbon dioxide. When shaken with water, it is hydrolysed to form carbon dioxide and hydrogen sulphide (H_2S).

Carbon disulphide is reduced by hydrogen in the presence of a nickel catalyst to form methane and hydrogen sulphide.

(a) What is meant by the terms

(i) solvent

....

(ii) hydrolysed

....

(iii) reduction

....

....

(3 marks)

(b) (i) What evidence is there that carbon disulphide is a covalent compound?

....

(ii) Draw a dot (·) and cross (x) diagram (to represent electrons) to show the structure of a molecule of carbon disulphide. (Show only the outermost electrons.)

(3 marks)

(c) Complete the following equations, including state symbols:

(i) CS_2 (l) + O_2 (g) →

(ii) CS_2 (l) + H_2O (l) →

(iii) CS_2 (l) + H_2 (g) →

(6 marks)

(d) Suggest a method of obtaining sulphur from a mixture of sulphur dissolved in carbon disulphide. Mention any safety precautions you would take.

....

....

....

(3 marks)

Total: 15 marks

Longman
Examination Board

General Certificate of Secondary Education

Science (Double award)

Higher Paper 3

Time: 60 minutes

Instructions

■ Answer **all** the questions.

■ Write your answers in the spaces provided.

■ Use a blue or black ink or ball-point pen.

■ Show all stages in any calculations and state the units.

Information for candidates

■ The number of marks is given in brackets at the end of each question or part-question. The total mark for the question is given at the end of the question.

■ Marks will **not** be deducted for wrong answers.

■ This paper has 6 questions.

■ The maximum mark for this paper is 60.

Number	Mark
1.	
2.	
3.	
4.	
5.	
6.	

1. The diagram below shows a cross section of a dam wall.

Leave margin blank

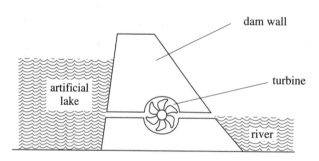

dam wall

turbine

artificial lake

river

(a) Why is the wall thicker at the bottom than at the top?

pressure increases with depth

(1 mark)

(b) The outside wall slopes outwards (away from the artificial lake); the inner wall is almost vertical. Suggest a reason for this structure.

more pressure from artifical lake, water has to be kept down

(2 marks)

(c) The wall of a dam is usually curved. Which way does it curve and why?

....

....

(2 marks)

After the Kariba dam was built, water was allowed to flow causing Lake Kariba to form.

(d) (i) While the lake was filling, earth tremors were felt over 200 miles away. What caused these tremors?

.... *the water crashing into lake* ....

(ii) Suggest one ecological problem that is caused by building a dam.

.... *Might need to mae house* ....

(2 marks)

(e) Explain why a bubble of air released at the base of the dam increases in volume as it rises up through the water.

.... *because there is less pressure pushing* ....

.... *on it as you go up* ....

(2 marks)

(f) (i) What sort of energy is stored in the water in a dam?

.... *potential* ....

(ii) In the dam, what is the energy named in (f) (i) transferred into?

.... *electrical* ....

(2 marks)

Total: 11 marks

2. The diagram below shows a simplified version of a solar water heater.

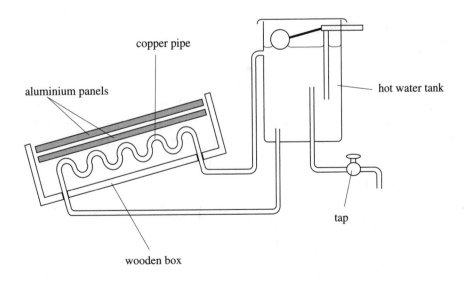

copper pipe

aluminium panels

hot water tank

tap

wooden box

Turn over

(a) Suggest why the following materials are used:

   (i) aluminium for the faces of the panels

       attracts sun, emits it

   (ii) copper for the piping

       conducts elec

   (iii) wood for the base of the panel

       does not conduct it away

                               (3 marks)

(b) The aluminium on the panel is usually made up of two layers. Suggest a reason for the two layers. *if any is not absorbed reabsorbed*

                                  (2 marks)

(c) (i) Why must the bottom of the hot water storage tank be above the level of the top of the panel?

   (ii) How does the heat energy get into the hot water tank?

       convection currents

                                  (2 marks)

(d) Explain why fewer houses in Europe use solar power than in Japan.

       less max sun

                                  (1 mark)

The graph below shows how the voltage from a solar cell drops as the current is increased.

(e) (i) Calculate the amount of energy that enters the panel (size = 0.002 m²) per second if 1000
Joules falls per second on each square metre of the Earth's surface.

$\mathcal{E} =$

....

....

(2 marks)

(ii) Calculate the power output at B.

....

....

(2 marks)

(iii) Calculate the efficiency of energy conversion at point B.

....

....

(2 marks)

(f) Solar power is a form of renewable energy source. Name two other renewable energy sources.

....

....

(2 marks)

Total: 16 marks

3. The experiment shown in the diagram below was set up to investigate radioactivity.

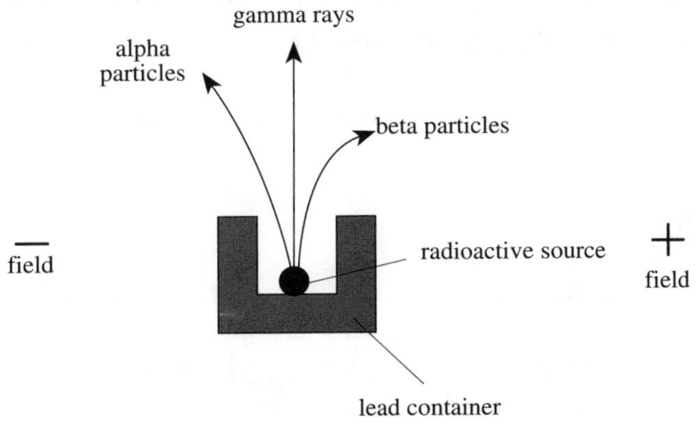

It was found that alpha particles were attracted slightly to the negative field; beta particles were
attracted greatly towards the positive field and there was no effect on gamma rays.

(a) (i) What deductions can you make about alpha particles, beta particles and gamma rays from
this experiment?

.... alpha (+) ....

.... gamma (o) .... alpha leaver than ....

.... beta (-) .... Beta ....

(4 marks)

Turn over

Leave margin blank

(ii) What is an alpha particle?

.... helium nuclei rag

(1 mark)

(iii) What is a beta particle?

.... electron

(1 mark)

(b) What instrument could be used to measure radioactivity?

.... gaega muller counter

(1 mark)

(c) Suggest why the radioactive source is placed in a lead container.

.... Gamma, Beta, alpha will get through

(1 mark)

new point

(d) (i) Define 'half-life'.

.... time taken for radioactive atom to decay

(1 mark)

(ii) The half-life of carbon-14 is 5700 years. How many years is equivalent to three half-lives of carbon?

2850, 1425, 7125 ... no ... 5700 × 3

(1 mark)

(iii) Carbon-14 has been used to date various articles. Suggest a reason why it is impractical to use this method for remains more than 40000 years old.

.... it would already be consid

(1 mark)

(e) Give two uses of radioactivity.

.... Tracers eg for iodine - thyroid gland
.... leaks

(2 marks)

Total: 13 marks

4. A student tried to measure the approximate distance of the moon from the Earth by asking a friend to use a coin so that it just covered the surface of the moon (see diagram below).

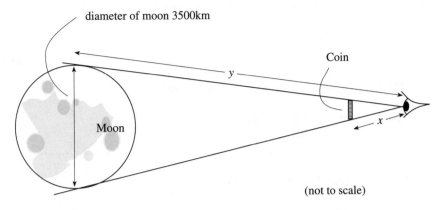

diameter of moon 3500km

Coin

y

Moon

x

(not to scale)

The diameter of the coin used was 2 cm, the diameter of the moon is 3500 km.

On day 1 the distance *x* was 2.00 m and on day 130 the distance *x* was 2.29 m.

(a) (i) Calculate the distance (*y*) of the moon from the earth, to the nearest 100 km on day 1.

350 000

....

....

....

(3 marks)

(ii) On day 130 is the moon (A) nearer the Earth; (B) further away; or (C) the same distance from the Earth? Explain your answer.

400750 further away

(1 mark)

(b) (i) Draw a diagram showing the force of the moon's gravitational pull on the Earth.

(1 mark)

(ii) Explain how this brings about the rise and fall of the sea (tides).

....

(1 mark)

(iii) Explain why high tides and low tides appear at the same time on opposite sides of the Earth.

....

(1 mark)

(iv) Explain why there are two high tides and two low tides a day.

....

....

(2 marks)

Turn over

(c) What is the difference between a moon and a comet?

....

....

(2 marks)

(d) Syncom 4 is a communication satellite. It follows a *geosynchronous orbit*.

  (i) Explain what is meant by a *geosynchronous orbit*.

.............*Stays still*...

  (ii) Give one advantage of this type of communication link.

.............*Uninterupted signal*...

(2 marks)

Total: 13 marks

5. In each of the sentences below, ONE word has been used incorrectly. Identify the word that is wrong and state the correct word that should have been used.

  (i)   A thermometer is a temperature-dependent resistor.

    wrong word ...*thermom*... correct word ...*mistor*...

  (ii) Change in speed of light from one medium to another causes reflection.

    wrong word ...*reflection*... correct word ...*refraction*...

  (iii) Asteroids are a group of rocks that appear between the orbits of Jupiter and Saturn.

    wrong word ...*Saturn*... correct word ...*Mars*...

(3 marks)

Total: 3 marks

6. The graph below shows the increase in the length of a spring for different weights. The line X was obtained using another material.

(a) Whose law is being obeyed by the straight line portion of the graph for the spring?

............................Hookes..

(1 mark)

(b) What is meant by the phrase *elastic limit*?

............when it has limit that will go back to original slope, pass no.

(1 mark)

(c) Give a practical everyday use of the law stated in (a).

............................Spring..

(1 mark)

(d) Suggest, with a reason, an identity for material X.

....

(1 mark)

Total: 4 marks

Turn over

Solutions to practice papers

Each * represents 1 mark. Make sure your answer is correct before you award yourself the mark – if you are not sure ask your teacher or another responsible person. Text written in brackets is NOT required to score the mark.

The tip at the end of each question will help you with your revision.

Solutions to Foundation 1

1.

Part	Name	Function
A	mouth *	breaks down starch and sugar *
B	liver *	either removal of poisons, or storage of glucose * (there are other functions – check with your teacher)
C	stomach *	digests food * (pepsin breaks down protein)
D	rectum *	stores waste temporarily * (before it is ejected)
E	small intestine *	absorbs (soluble) food * (such as fat, sugar)

Total: 10 marks

TIP

Learn to identify the various organs of the body and their functions. Others you may be asked about include the oesophagus (gullet), large intestine and pancreas. Note that in this question the arrow points to the mouth NOT the oesophagus. All animals have similar systems – you will observe how similar the digestive tract of the pig is to that of humans.

2. (a) only plants are able to convert energy from the sun into food *   **1 mark**

(b) direction of energy flow through the food web *   **1 mark**

(c) (i) caterpillars, rabbits, mice, snails * (must get all four correct) (ii) owl, snake * (must get both right)   **2 marks**

(d) producers *   **1 mark**

(e) (i)   **   **2 marks**

(ii)   **   **2 marks**

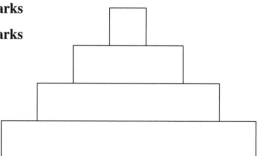

(in *each* case 2 marks if shape given in diagram; 1 mark if this pyramid is inverted.)

(f) a pyramid of numbers does not distinguish between the differences in size of organisms e.g. one tree is given the same value as one aphid – biomass overcomes this problem *   **1 mark**

Total: 10 marks

> Herbivores only eat plants; carnivores are meat eaters. The arrows represent the direction of energy flow through the system – a food chain is the representation of a single energy pathway, e.g. from the above diagram one food chain would be plants → mice → snake → owl → hawk. The pyramid of biomass can also be misleading, e.g. in water systems the producers are small in size, but have a high turnover rate. A better system is the pyramid of energy.

3. chloroplasts * chlorophyll * photosynthesis * carbon dioxide * oxygen * Sun * carbon dioxide * soil * roots * leaves *   **Total: 10 marks**

> For photosynthesis to occur, sunlight must fall on the chlorophyll contained in the leaves where it is absorbed. Initially glucose is formed, but this is turned into starch so that the plant can store the food. Starch can be shown to be present by using iodine – a blue-black colour confirms the presence of starch. Make sure that you know the differences between plant cells and animal cells.

4. (a)

Part of the breathing system	What is does
alveoli	sites of gaseous exchange
diaphragm *	a muscle sheet
intercostal muscles	**muscles that raise and lower the rib cage** *
lungs *	organs of respiration
ribs	**protect the lungs** *
trachea *	connects lungs to mouth and nose

5 marks

(b) breathing is the process of taking air into the lungs and removing air from the lungs *; respiration is the release of energy from the breakdown of food molecules within cells *   **2 marks**

(c) speeds up the interchange of gases *   **1 mark**

(d) (i) nitrogen is an unreactive gas *   **1 mark**

(ii) oxygen reacts with carbohydrates in the blood and is thus reduced *; carbon dioxide is formed in this process, thus increasing the volume of carbon dioxide *   **2 marks**

(iii) exhaled air still contains oxygen *   **1 mark**

(e) smoking can deprive the foetus of oxygen *   **1 mark**   **Total: 13 marks**

> Make sure you learn how we adapt our breathing to cope with exercise.

5. (a) reflex *   (b) brain *; spinal cord *   (c) (ii) tongue *   (iii) skin *   (iv) skin *   **6 marks**

(d) (i) focusing *   (ii) light sensitive layer *   (iii) carries impulses from retina to brain *   **3 marks**

Total: 9 marks

6. (a) 25 * (b) 32 % ($\frac{8}{25} \times 100$) * **2 marks**

(c) any two such as height, weight, shoe size, etc * * **2 marks**

(d) (i) any from (c) above, or size of leaves etc. (Continuous variation gives a normal distribution curve, i.e. most in the middle of the curve and fewer distributed evenly on either side of the middle of the curve.) * **1 mark**

(ii) blood group. (Discontinuous variation cannot be altered by environmental factors during the lifetime of the species.) * **1 mark**

(e) any two from: environment; inheritance; mutations * * **2 marks**   **Total: 8 marks**

Solutions to Foundation 2

1. (a) (i) any element from sodium to argon inclusive * (ii) bromine * (iii) argon * (iv) either helium, or neon, or argon * (v) sulphur * (vi) aluminium * (vii) nitrogen, oxygen, argon *; correct order *   **8 marks**

(b) chlorine has two isotopes, * (Cl^{35} and Cl^{37}); the relative atomic mass is a combination of these two numbers * **2 marks**   **Total: 10 marks**

2. (a)   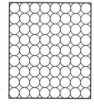   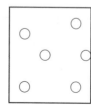   regular order – solid *
far apart – gases *
irregular in gases *

    solid   gas   **3 marks**

(b) particles spread out (more) *; particles move faster *   **2 marks**

(c) (i) freezing * (ii) sublimation *   **2 marks**   **Total: 7 marks**

> **TIP**
>
> Learn that particles in solids are arranged regularly, close together and vibrate in fixed positions; in liquids the particles are in clusters, fairly close together and move around; in gases they move around freely and are far apart from one another. Learn all the changes in state. Very few substances sublime.

3.

Type of change	Example
endothermic reaction	hydrochloric acid plus sodium hydroxide
neutralisation	adding potassium nitrate to water
displacement	propane to propene plus hydrogen
exothermic reaction	heating ammonium chloride to give ammonia and hydrogen chloride which recombine on cooling
hydration	glucose in the presence of enzymes giving ethanol and carbon dioxide
fermentation	anhydrous copper(II) sulphate reacting with water
reduction	hydrogen burning in chlorine to give hydrogen chloride
reversible reaction	sodium sulphate reacting with barium chloride to give insoluble barium sulphate and sodium chloride
precipitation	iron reacting with copper(II) sulphate
cracking	magnesium burning in oxygen

One mark for each line   **Total: 9 marks**

> **TIP**
>
> Try to learn to distinguish between all the different types of reaction. Dissolving salts in water is an endothermic reaction. All reactions involving burning in oxygen are exothermic reactions – thus the reaction of magnesium with oxygen is both oxidation and exothermic. Displacement involves one element displacing another element, whereas precipitation involves two soluble compounds reacting to form an insoluble compound.

4. (a) aluminium oxide + magnesium → aluminium + magnesium oxide

left hand side correct *; right hand side correct *   **2 marks**

(b) sodium, potassium, barium (must be a metal high in the reactivity series) *; it is above magnesium in the reactivity series (or more reactive than aluminium) *   **2 marks**

(c) Group 3 * and period 3 *   **2 marks**

(d) (i) to stop either aluminium or magnesium, or both, catching fire *

(ii) (greater surface area therefore) speeds up the reaction *   **2 marks**

(e) protons 13 *; neutrons 14 *; electrons 10 *   **3 marks**

(f) electrolysis *   **1 mark**   **Total: 12 marks**

5. (a) (i) sedimentary – burial of weathered rock *; under pressure *

     (ii) igneous – magma rising up from mantle *; cooling and solidifying *

     (iii) metamorphic – (rocks buried deep underground, structure changed by) high temperature * and high pressure *   **6 marks**

  (b) either limestone or sandstone, etc. *; either granite or basalt, etc. *; either marble or slate, etc. *

                                                            3 marks

  (c) (i) Sedimentary * (ii) each layer of rock will contain fossils of plants and animals that lived at the time that the sediment was laid down * thus knowing when the plants and animals lived one can determine the age of the rocks *   **3 marks**

  (d) crystals at X cool more quickly than those at Y *   **1 mark**

  (e) (i) water in the cracks in the rock expands on freezing and forces the rocks apart *   (ii) acid rain reacts with rocks such as limestone *   **2 marks**   **Total: 15 marks**

6. (a) either in natural gas, or in waste dumps, or other correct suggestion *   **1 mark**

  (b) the storage area must be kept well ventilated * to prevent build up of ethene which could burn (explode) in air *   **2 marks**

  (c) carbon *; carbon monoxide *   **2 marks**

  (d) greenhouse *   **1 mark**

  (e) C_2H_4 *   **1 mark**   **Total: 7 marks**

Solutions to Foundation 3

1. (a) (i)   *   **1 mark**

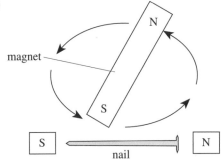

(ii) tie the string to the middle of the nail and hold it up so that it swings freely *; the nail will act as a compass and point north/south *   **2 marks**

(b) (i) the magnetic force * (ii) gravitational force *   **2 marks**

(iii) magnetism is induced in the other nails *; thus each nail becomes a magnet and is attracted to the others *   **2 marks**

(iv) see how many nails a magnet can pick up *; the more that are picked up – the stronger the magnet *   **2 marks**

(c) (i) the iron rod became magnetised and generated a stronger magnetic field *   (ii) by increasing the number of turns in the coil *   **2 marks**

(d) electric bell, or other suitable use *   **1 mark**   **Total: 12 marks**

> **TIP**
>
> Other methods of making a nail magnetic include placing it on a strong magnet, or placing it in an electrified coil (solenoid). A simple test to show that a piece of iron is a magnet is to see if it will attract other iron objects. Note that the two forces balance – there is the pull of the magnetic force and the pull of the gravitational force. Another way to increase the magnetic field of a coil is to increase the current flowing through the coil.

2. (a) (i) ✓ *   (ii) ✓ *   (iii) ✗ *   (iv) ✓ *   (v) ✓ *   **5 marks**

(b)

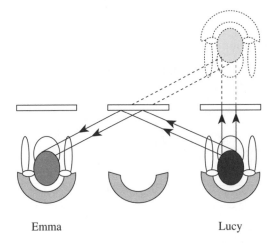

Emma   Lucy

straight lines *; Lucy's reflection in the correct position *; rays from reflection to Emma passing through central mirror *   **3 marks**

(c) (C) slightly lower *; light is refracted at the surface of water and air *; making the fish appear higher in the water than it really is * **3 marks**

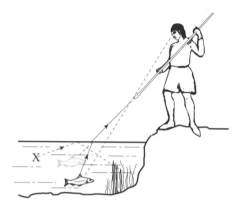

(d) total internal reflection * **1 mark** **Total: 12 marks**

TIP

An image in a mirror is virtual (cannot be put on a screen); is laterally inverted (your left eye appears as your right eye in a mirror); and is formed as far behind the mirror as the object is in front – however, the size of the object does not change if a plane mirror is used. When light comes into contact with an object (e.g. a mirror) part of it gets bounced back, part of it is absorbed. Light travels in straight lines – it is usual to draw light rays that form a virtual image as dotted lines. Refraction occurs at the surface of two mediums – when light travels from water to air it bends away from the normal. When light rays strike the surface of the water at an angle greater than 48° they are totally internally reflected (see above diagram).

3. (a) sound is a form of energy * **1 mark**

(b) sound does not travel through a vacuum * **1 mark**

(c) (i) sound with a frequency above the audible frequency * **1 mark**

(ii) sound is bounced off the floor of the sea *; the time taken for this to happen is measured *

2 marks

(iii) either foetal imaging in obstetrics; or echo-location in bats * **1 mark**

(d) (i) see diagram – same frequency *; larger amplitude * **2 marks**

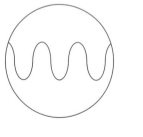 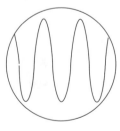

before   after

(ii) see diagram – smaller frequency *; same amplitude as (d) (i) *   **2 marks**

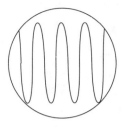

Total: 10 marks

4. (a) If they were placed in series then a fault in one heater would cause both not to work *. Both elements can function independently of each other in a parallel circuit *.   **2 marks**

   (b) Voltmeter across ends of element *   **1 mark**

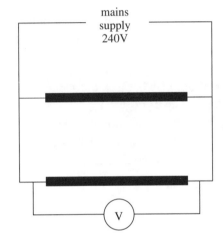

   (c) Two switches *; in positions shown on diagram *   **2 marks**

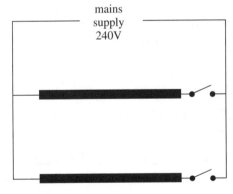

   (d) 5 A *; current in circuit is 4 A ($\frac{240}{60}$ amps) *   **2 marks**

   (e) (i) earth *   (ii) live *   **2 marks**

   (f) fuse made of low melting point alloy *; if current is too high, fuse melts and current cannot flow *   **2 marks**

   (g) power = 240 × 4 = 960 watts = 0.96 kilowatts *; cost = 0.96 × 10 × 7 = £6.72 *   **2 marks**

Total: 13 marks

TIP

In series, once one appliance fails all fail. You may have noticed this with certain Christmas tree lights, once one goes out they all go out. When a parallel circuit is used this does not happen. Your house is wired using parallel circuits, thus if one light goes out, the rest remain on. Current = voltage/resistance, i.e. 240/60 = 4 amps – thus a 5 amp fuse is used. Too high a fuse rating can cause severe damage (including fires). Cost of electricity = power × time × cost. Electricity is sold in kilowatt-hours.

5. (a) (i) Sun *   (ii) Mars *   (iii) Jupiter *   (iv) Pluto *   (v) orbits *   (vi) Mercury *
    (vii) moons *   **7 marks**

    (b) any two from planets do not produce light; planets are colder; planets orbit stars * *   **2 marks**
    Total: 9 marks

TIP

You must learn the names of the planets and their order from the Sun – the nearest is Mercury; the furthest is Pluto. Pluto is the only planet not in the same plane as the other planets. The Sun is the source of our heat and light energy – life on Earth exists only because of the Sun. The Sun is a star – it looks so big and bright to us because it is closer than any other star. It is the only star that is visible during daylight.

6. (a) potential energy *   (b) kinetic energy *   (c) air resistance is almost equal to gravitational pull *
    (d) hot air rises – (keeping the glider in the air longer) *   **Total: 4 marks**

TIP

Energy cannot be created or destroyed. Potential energy is gained in this case because the glider has climbed (potential energy is the energy of an object due to its make up or position, e.g chemical energy or a wound spring both possess potential energy). When the glider jumps, he starts moving, and thus potential energy is transferred into kinetic energy (energy of movement).

Solutions to Higher 1

1. (a) homeostasis *   **1 mark**

    (b) (i) cold day (little sweat but much urine) *   (ii) warm day (urine and sweat lost in roughly the same amounts) *   (iii) very hot day (more sweat than urine) *   **3 marks**

    (c) (i) sweating – the evaporation of water cools the skin *; the diameter of the skin's superficial capillaries increases and allows more blood through to be cooled *   **2 marks**

    (ii) waterproof layer *; germ-proof layer *   **2 marks**

    (d) (i) water not reabsorbed *; urine very dilute therefore pale in colour *   **2 marks**

    (ii) the water filtered out by the kidneys will be reabsorbed into the blood stream *; hence urine will be concentrated and darker in colour *   **2 marks**

    (e) (i) it removes waste products such as salts and urea *   (ii) it regulates the water content of the body fluids *   **2 marks**
    Total: 14 marks

TIP

Homeostasis is the control mechanism by which conditions are kept steady. The skin keeps the temperature steady and the kidneys keep the water level steady. Sweating does not occur evenly throughout the body; it increases with the number of sweat glands and with the amount of hair on the body. When it gets cold, the capillaries in the skin narrow and prevent the blood from being cooled. Small muscles in the skin, attached to hairs, make the hairs stand up on end and trap a layer of insulating air near the skin. If further cooling occurs we start shivering – the muscles as they move produce heat and warm our blood.

2. (a) axis labelled *; points labelled *; points correctly plotted *; straight line through points (and crossing the *x* and *y* axes) *   **4 marks**

   (b) energy value is inversely proportional to water content *   **1 mark**

   (c) 18.0 (kJ/kg) *   (d) the Sun *   (e) water *   **3 marks**   **Total: 8 marks**

> **TIP**
> This is a comprehension question – although not directly on the syllabus, you will be able to make your deductions. All energy comes in the first place from the Sun. A straight line graph sloping upwards indicates that there is a direct relationship between the two values being plotted; however, in this case the straight line graph slopes downwards, indicating an inverse relationship. The point where the line crosses the *x*-axis represents 100% water, which has little or no energy value.

3. (a) (i) alternative forms of a gene * (ii) units of heredity * (iii) haploid reproductive cells *   **3 marks**

   (b) his ideas were too advanced for the period in which he lived, or something similar *   **1 mark**

   (c)
   (i)    *

   (ii)    *

   (iii) 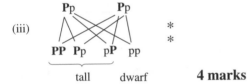   *
        *
        4 marks

   (d) 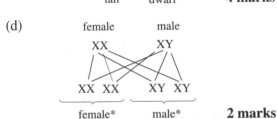   **2 marks**

   (e) (i) a programme used with animals or plants to select and stabilise characteristics which are useful to man * (ii) producing genetically identical offspring *   **2 marks**   **Total: 12 marks**

> **TIP**
> Alleles are different forms of genes that can be either dominant or recessive. For example the allele that produces brown eyes is more dominant than the allele that produces green eyes. Make sure you understand the answers given to this question. Genetic diseases that may be inherited include cystic fibrosis and sickle cell anaemia. Both of these are carried by a recessive gene – but if your parents are carriers you stand a 1 in 4 chance of inheriting the disease. Mendel was the father of genetics – the true worth of his work was not realised until the early 1900s. Cloning was originally the production of offspring by asexual reproduction and could only occur in simpler plants and animals. As you may have read in your newspapers, it is now possible to clone larger animals such as sheep and calves. Owners of race horses and 'show' dogs go in for selective breeding – they try to get all the best characteristics into the offspring.

4. (a) sunlight * and chlorophyll *   **2 marks**

   (b) $6CO_2 + 6H_2O \rightarrow C_6H_{12}O_6 + 6O_2$

      * for correct formulae; * for correctly balancing the equation   **2 marks**

   (c) (i) large surface area *; helps to absorb either more sunlight, or more carbon dioxide *

      (ii) light can pass through *; either prevents excess water loss, or prevents diseases entering leaves *

      (iii) contain chloroplasts, and therefore being near the surface increases rate of photosynthesis *; being stacked in columns allows passage of light into cell *   **6 marks**

   (d) (i) an increase in carbon dioxide increases the rate of oxygen given off *   **1 mark**

      (ii) photosynthesis depends on the wavelength of light *; the longer the wavelength the more oxygen is given off *   **2 marks**

   (e) (i) starch *   (ii) lipids *   (iii) cellulose *   **3 marks**   **Total: 16 marks**

> **TIP**
>
> Photosynthesis gets its name from two Greek words *photo* = light and *synthesis* = to combine up, i.e. photosynthesis is the process by which plants manufacture their own food with the help of sunlight. The structure of leaves is very important; they have evolved to be very efficient at converting carbon dioxide and water into carbohydrates and oxygen. Green plants are so good at removing carbon dioxide that the level of carbon dioxide in the air remains at around 0.03%. However, we must not be complacent – the level is slowly increasing, giving rise to the greenhouse effect. You should be able to predict that photosynthesis occurs more slowly in ultra-violet light and more rapidly in infra-red light. Glucose has many functions in a leaf including helping to produce amino-acids.

5. (a) A – aorta *; B – pulmonary vein *; C – left atrium *; D – vena cava *   **4 marks**

   (b) lungs *   (c) towards the heart *   high *   thick and elastic (to withstand high pressure) *   **4 marks**

   (d) (i) they would thicken * (deposit of fat on the lumen)   (ii) likely to have a heart attack *   **2 marks**

                                                               Total: 10 marks

> **TIP**
>
> Blood flows from the pulmonary vein, through the left atrium into the left ventricle to the aorta. The heart has arteries and veins attached to it to supply blood containing food and oxygen to the heart muscles. If this does not occur (because of furring up of arteries – one of the side effects of smoking), the heart stops functioning. This is called a heart attack or heart failure. Sometimes babies are born with a 'hole in their heart'. This means that the left ventricle is joined to the right ventricle by a hole. Such babies will suffer from a lack of energy.

Solutions to Higher 2

1. (a) hydrochloric acid *   (b) aluminium or other reactive metal *   (c) sandstone or limestone *   (d) any Group 1, 2 or 3 metal with Group 6 or 7 element *   **Total: 4 marks**

2. (a) (i) C_9H_{20} *   (ii) between 190 °C and 195 °C *   **2 marks**

   (b) hexane *   **1 mark**

   (c) decane, undecane and dodecane; * * for three correct and * for two correct   **2 marks**

(d) (i) to prevent liquid running back and cracking the tube *   (ii) to stop water entering the apparatus ('suck back') *   (iii) butane *   **3 marks**

(e) (i) a small molecule that can be polymerised (to make a large molecule) *   **1 mark**

(ii)

or CH_3CHCH_2

double bond *; formula correct *   **2 marks**

(iii)

single bonds *; 6 carbon atoms joined together *; idea that the structure continues *   **3 marks**

(iv) polypropene has a very high carbon content *   **1 mark**   **Total: 15 marks**

> **TIP**
> For a homologous series, in this case the alkane series, there is a regular change in physical properties. Thus melting point, boiling point and density increase. Members also have a general formula. In this case C_nH_{2n+2}. Nonene is C_9H_{18} – if this is subtracted from $C_{13}H_{28}$ we are left with C_4H_{10} which is butane. Compounds with a high percentage of carbon burn with a smoky flame. Thus C_2H_2 burns with a smokier flame than C_2H_4, which is smokier than C_2H_6.

3. (a) $2H^+ (aq) + 2e(electrons) \rightarrow H_2 (g)$

equation correct *; state symbols correct *   **2 marks**

(b) oxygen * given off reacts with carbon electrode to form carbon dioxide *; carbon dioxide reacts with lime water to form calcium carbonate *   **3 marks**

(c) soluble * calcium hydrogencarbonate formed *   **2 marks**

(d) calcium carbonate *   **1 mark**

(e) calcium hydroxide is less soluble in hot water than in cold water *   **1 mark**

(f) (i) to neutralise acidic soil *   (ii) it is much cheaper than sodium hydroxide *   **2 marks**

Total: 11 marks

> **TIP**
> Lime-water is used as a test for carbon dioxide. The action of excess carbon dioxide is similar to the reaction of rain water with limestone, producing hard water. It causes temporary hardness because the calcium ions are removed when the water is boiled. Calcium hydroxide is very unusual, its solubility in water decreases as the temperature increases. Plants grow best in soil that has a pH between 6 and 8. Calcium hydroxide is also good for soil that contains clay.

4. (a) (i) water *   (ii) a mixture of hydrogen and air is explosive *   **2 marks**

(b) (i) mass of test tube empty *; mass of test tube plus oxide of copper *; mass of test tube plus copper *   **3 marks**

(ii) axis and scale used correct *; points plotted correctly *; straight line graph *; axis labelled correctly *   **4 marks**

(iii) F *   **1 mark**

(c) 6.4 g *   **1 mark**

(d) $\dfrac{6.4}{64}$ moles of copper react with $\dfrac{1.6}{16}$ mole of oxygen *

0.1 moles of copper react with 0.1 moles of oxygen *

1 mole of copper reacts with 1 mole of oxygen, hence formula is CuO *   **3 marks**

(e) lead or any metal low in the reactivity series *   **1 mark**   **Total: 15 marks**

> **TIP**
>
> Hydrogen is a very explosive gas – care must be taken when using it. The only way you can work out the mass of oxygen used is to subtract the mass of the test tube plus copper from the mass of the test tube plus the oxide of copper. Copper is a transition metal and forms two oxides: copper(I) oxide (Cu_2O) and copper(II) oxide (CuO). Formulae are worked out using mole ratios.

5. (a) (i) a liquid that is used to dissolve substances *   (ii) reacting with water *   (iii) addition of hydrogen, or removal of oxygen, or reduction in valency gains of electrons *   **3 marks**

(b) (i) it has a low boiling point *   (ii) 4 electrons around C and 6 electrons around S *,   sharing 2 pairs of electrons *   **3 marks**

(c) (i) CS_2 (l) + $3O_2$ → CO_2 (g) + $2SO_2$ (g) * *

(ii) CS_2 (l) + $2H_2O$ → CO_2 (g) + $2H_2S$ (g) * *

(iii) CS_2 (l) + $4H_2$ (g) → CH_4 (g) + $2H_2S$ (g) * *   In each case left hand side 1 mark, right hand side 1 mark   **6 marks**

(d) heat in a beaker of hot water *; make sure no flames are near *; CS_2 will evaporate leaving dry sulphur *   **3 marks**   **Total: 15 marks**

> **TIP**
>
> Sulphur and oxygen are in the same group of the Periodic Table and therefore you would expect them to have similar properties and to form similar compounds. The structure of carbon disulphide is very similar to that of carbon dioxide. You were told the products of the reactions in the introduction – you should have used this information when answering part (c). Because carbon disulphide has a low boiling point it will easily vaporise.

Solutions to Higher 3

1. (a) pressure increases with depth, therefore the bottom of the dam has to be stronger than the top *   **1 mark**

(b) the slope acts as a buttress – i.e. it helps the wall to resist the force of the water *; this is not required on the inner wall and would add to the cost of building the dam *   **2 marks**

(c) towards the artificial lake *; this gives the wall more strength *   **2 marks**

(d) (i) the increasing weight of the water *   (ii) resettlement of the inhabitants (both people and animals) *   **2 marks**

(e) pressure decreases as the bubble rises *; volume is directly proportional to pressure *   **2 marks**

(f) (i) potential energy *   (ii) electrical energy *   **2 marks**   **Total: 11 marks**

2. (a) (i) good conductor of heat * (ii) easily bent * (iii) good insulator *   **3 marks**

    (b) prevents heat lost by radiation (heat reflected back from surface) *, and by convection (air cannot escape) *   **2 marks**

    (c) (i) water would drain out of solar panels *   (ii) by convection currents *   **2 marks**

    (d) either cost of solar panels, or there is more sun in Japan *   **1 mark**

    (e) (i) $1000 \times 0.002 = 2.0$ * watts *   **2 marks**

    (ii) 0.5×0.4 * $= 0.20$ watts *   **2 marks**

    (iii) $\dfrac{0.2}{2.0} \times 100$ * $= 10\%$ *   **2 marks**

    (f) any two from wood; hydro-electric power; wave power; tidal power; wind power * *   **2 marks**

    Total: 16 marks

3. (a) (i) alpha particles are positively charged * beta particles are negatively charged *; no charge on gamma rays *; alpha particles are larger than beta particles*   **4 marks**

    (ii) helium ion $^{4}_{2}\text{He}^{2+}$ *   (iii) electron *   **2 marks**

    (b) Geiger counter *   **1 mark**

    (c) to prevent radioactive particles escaping from the sides of the container *   **1 mark**

    (d) (i) time taken for half a given number of radioactive atoms to decay to different atoms *   **1 mark**

    (ii) $5700 \times 3 = 17\,100$ years *   **1 mark**

    (iii) value of radioactive count becomes too small to measure *   **1 mark**

    (e) any two from: treatment of cancer; tracers in medicine; tracers in industry; quality control in industry * *   **2 marks**   **Total: 13 marks**

4. (a) (i) 2 cm = 0.02 m *

$$\frac{3500}{0.02} = \frac{y}{2.00} \quad *$$

y = 350 000 km * **3 marks**

(ii) (B) Further away – the distance of the coin from the eye is directly proportional to the distance of the Earth from the moon* (this can be expressed in a number of different ways). **1 mark**

(b) (i) the gravity of the moon shown on the diagram correctly, i.e. pulling towards the moon *

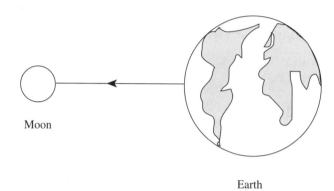

Earth

1 mark

(ii) the gravitational force of the moon attracts the sea towards it * **1 mark**

(iii) on one side of the Earth the moon will pull the sea towards it; on the other side of the Earth it will have no effect * **1 mark**

(iv) the Earth spins on its axis once a day *; at one particular moment the sea at that point will be facing the moon and 12 hours later the same point will be on the opposite side, away from the moon * **2 marks**

(c) Moons are in orbits around planets *; comets are in orbits around the Sun * **2 marks**

(d) (i) takes 24 hours to go round the Earth * (ii) get an uninterrupted signal * **2 marks**

Total: 13 marks

TIP

The calculation is based on similar triangles. The moon is not on a circular orbit around the Earth; sometimes it is nearer to the Earth than others. If we could look down on the Earth we would see the following

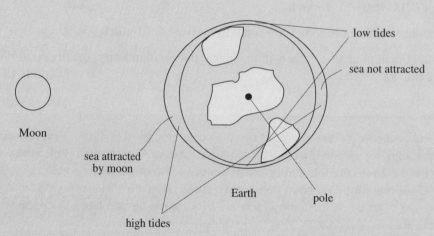

You will see the idea of high tides and low tides. Learn the differences between moons, planets and comets. Geosynchronous orbits stay in the same place over the Earth's surface.

5. (i) thermometer; thermistor *   (ii) reflection; refraction *   (iii) Saturn; Mars*   **Total: 3 marks**

TIP

Thermometers measure temperature, they rely on the expansion of liquids to measure temperature. High temperatures are measured with thermistors.
There is no change in the speed of light when reflection occurs.
Asteroids are a group of rock debris that occur between the orbits of Jupiter and Mars.

---

6. (a) Hooke's law *   **1 mark**

    (b) The point beyond which Hooke's law is no longer obeyed. The spring in this case stretches more with each additional load than is predicted by Hooke's law. *   **1 mark**

    (c) spring weighing machine, or similar answer *   **1 mark**

    (d) elastic – the material suddenly stretches, and the line is not straight – i.e. Hooke's law is not obeyed *   **1 mark**   **Total: 4 marks**

TIP

Hooke's law applies to any solid that undergoes stress. A tennis ball when it hits a tennis racket gets squashed, but it retains its shape. If the force was such that the rubber of the ball exceeded the elastic limit of the ball, the ball would go out of shape. Substances that stretch, like rubber, do not obey Hooke's law.

How well did you do?

Here is a guide to the grades you might obtain, after adding together the marks you obtained for the Foundation and Higher papers. The maximum mark is 180.

Foundation		Higher	
Mark	**Grade**	**Mark**	**Grade**
>144	C	>161	A*
126–143	D	144–161	A
108–125	E	126–143	B
90–107	F	108–125	C
72–89	G	90–107	D
<72	U	<90	U

If you do not reach grade G on the Foundation Tier papers you will be unclassified (U) and the result will not appear on your GCSE certificate. If you fail to reach grade D on the Higher Tier papers you will be unclassified (U) and the result will not appear on your GCSE certificate.

This is why it is important that you enter at the right level.

	Group 1	Group 2											Group 3	Group 4	Group 5	Group 6	Group 7	Group 0
							H Hydrogen											4 He Helium 2
Period 2	7 Li Lithium 3	9 Be Beryllium 4											11 B Boron 5	12 C Carbon 6	14 N Nitrogen 7	16 O Oxygen 8	19 F Fluorine 9	20 Ne Neon 10
Period 3	23 Na Sodium 11	24 Mg Magnesium 12											27 Al Aluminium 13	28 Si Silicon 14	31 P Phosphorus 15	32 S Sulphur 16	35.5 Cl Chlorine 17	40 Ar Argon 18
Period 4	39 K Potassium 19	40 Ca Calcium 20	45 Sc Scandium 21	48 Ti Titanium 22	51 V Vanadium 23	52 Cr Chromium 24	55 Mn Manganese 25	56 Fe Iron 26	59 Co Cobalt 27	59 Ni Nickel 28	63.5 Cu Copper 29	65 Zn Zinc 30	70 Ga Gallium 31	73 Ge Germanium 32	75 As Arsenic 33	79 Se Selenium 34	80 Br Bromine 35	84 Kr Krypton 36
Period 5	85 Rb Rubidium 37	88 Sr Strontium 38	89 Y Yttrium 39	91 Zr Zirconium 40	93 Nb Niobium 41	96 Mo Molybdenum 42	Tc Technetium 43	101 Ru Ruthenium 44	103 Rh Rhodium 45	106 Pd Palladium 46	108 Ag Silver 47	112 Cd Cadmium 48	115 In Indium 49	119 Sn Tin 50	122 Sb Antimony 51	128 Te Tellurium 52	127 I Iodine 53	131 Xe Xenon 54
Period 6	133 Cs Caesium 55	137 Ba Barium 56	139 La Lanthanum 57	178 Hf Hafnium 72	181 Ta Tantalum 73	184 W Tungsten 74	186 Re Rhenium 75	190 Os Osmium 76	192 Ir Iridium 77	195 Pt Platinum 78	197 Au Gold 79	201 Hg Mercury 80	204 Tl Thallium 81	207 Pb Lead 82	209 Bi Bismuth 83	Po Polonium 84	At Astatine 85	222 Rn Radon 86
Period 7	Fr Francium 87	226 Ra Radium 88	227 Ac Actinium 89															

Lanthanum series

140 Ce Cerium 58	141 Pr Praseodymium 59	144 Nd Neodymium 60	Pm Promethium 61	150 Sm Samarium 62	152 Eu Europium 63	157 Gd Gadolinium 64	159 Tb Terbium 65	162 Dy Dysprosium 66	165 Ho Holmium 67	167 Er Erbium 68	169 Tm Thulium 69	173 Yb Ytterbium 70	175 Lu Lutetium 71

Actinium series

232 Th Thorium 90	231 Pa Protactinium 91	238 U Uranium 92	Np Neptunium 93	Pu Plutonium 94	Am Americium 95	Cm Curium 96	Bk Berkelium 97	Cf Californium 98	Es Einsteinium 99	Fm Fermium 100	Md Mendelevium 101	No Nobelium 102	Lr Lowrencium 103

·58 – 57 Lanthanum series
†90 – 103 Actinium series

Elements for which no relative atomic mass is shown are not naturally occurring.